ABSTRACT STUDIO
ISSUE No.
37
3.99 US

TERRY MOORE

RACHEL RISING

"WOMAN IS THE ONLY CREATURE IN NATURE
THAT HUNTS DOWN ITS HUNTERS AND
DEVOURS THE PREY ALIVE."

—ABRAHAM MILLER

FOR A FEW THOUSAND DOLLARS, YOU CAN HAVE CREMATED ASHES TAKEN INTO SPACE.

BUT A WHOLE BODY?

NASA'S NOT GOING TO DO THAT. BUT ZOE SAID THE RUSSIANS WOULD.

"RUSSIA, CHINA, INDIA, FRANCE, SPACE X,.."

"A LOT OF PEOPLE GO TO SPACE," SHE SAID, "AND THEY ALL CARRY FREIGHT."

"ALL WE HAVE TO DO IS FIND MALUS, PUT HIM IN A BOX, PAY SOMEBODY TO TAKE IT INTO ORBIT AND PUSH IT OUT TO SPACE."

THEN THE DEMON WHO CANNOT DIE WOULD SPEND ETERNITY DRIFTING THROUGH NOTHING.

THE THING IS, I'M NOT SURE GETTING RID OF MALUS WILL SAVE US. HE SAID ZOE IS JUST ONE OF MANY BRANCHES. WHAT IF ONE OF THE OTHER OPTIONS HAS ALREADY BEEN BORN? WHAT IF THEY ALL HAVE?

FOR ALL WE KNOW, MALUS COULD HAVE DOZENS OR HUNDREDS OF CHILDREN OUT THERE; EVERY ONE OF THEM A LITTLE ANTI-CHRIST READY TO BURN IT ALL DOWN.

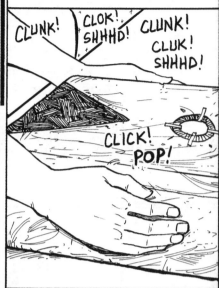

CLUNK!   CLOK! SHHHD!   CLUNK!
                         CLUK!
                         SHHHD!
        CLICK!
        POP!

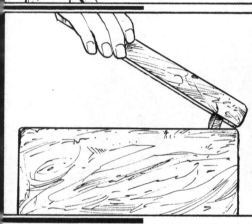

SO ALL OUR PLANS TO FIND MALUS, CATCH HIM, AND GET RID OF HIM FOREVER... IT COULD ALL BE A WASTE OF TIME. AND MAYBE THAT'S WHAT HE WANTS. MAYBE MALUS WANTS US TO CHASE HIM, LIKE A MOTHER LEADING PREDATORS AWAY FROM THE NEST. I MEAN, THIS IS A DEMON WHO HAS BEEN HIDING FOR MILLENIA. WHY DID HE COME OUT OF HIDING? AND WHY NOW?

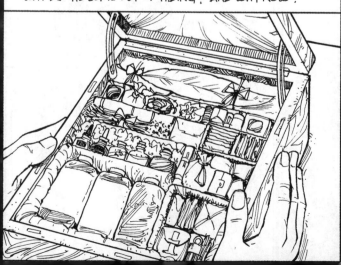

MY FEAR IS, WE'LL CHASE OUR FOX INTO A HOLE THAT CRACKS THE GATES OF HELL WIDE OPEN.
I THINK WE'LL FIND MALUS BECAUSE HE WANTS US TO FIND HIM. THE QUESTION IS—

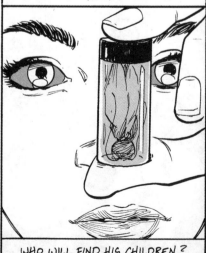

WHO WILL FIND HIS CHILDREN?

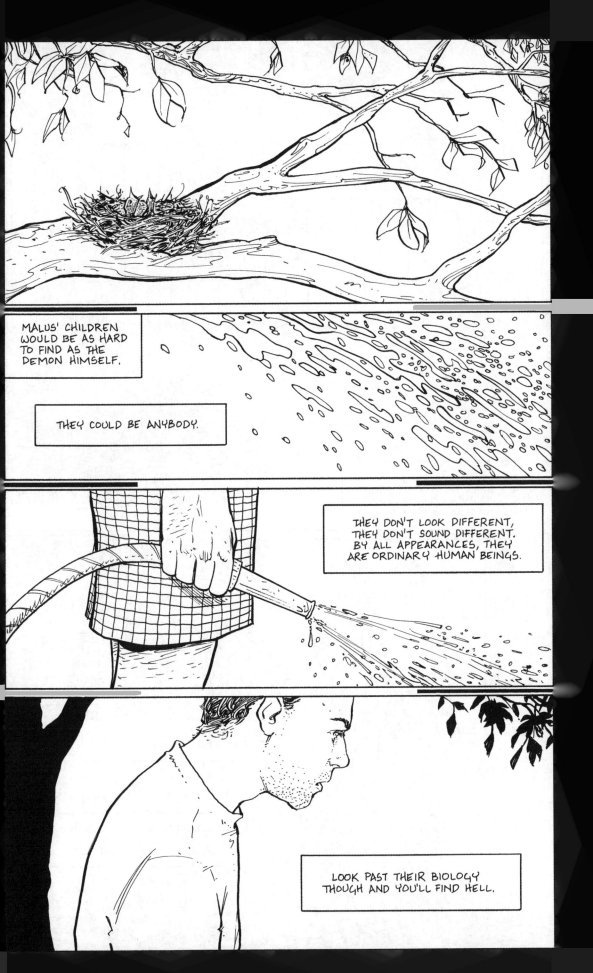

MALUS' CHILDREN WOULD BE AS HARD TO FIND AS THE DEMON HIMSELF.

THEY COULD BE ANYBODY.

THEY DON'T LOOK DIFFERENT, THEY DON'T SOUND DIFFERENT. BY ALL APPEARANCES, THEY ARE ORDINARY HUMAN BEINGS.

LOOK PAST THEIR BIOLOGY THOUGH AND YOU'LL FIND HELL.

NOT ALL OF MALUS' OFF-SPRING WOULD BEAR FRUIT. ODDS ARE, SOME WOULD BE CRIMINALS AND WASTE THEIR LIVES IN PRISON.

WHILE OTHERS WOULD MISFIRE AND SELF-DESTRUCT

TORMENTED BY THEIR OWN WICKED DESIRES THAT GO AGAINST HUMAN INSTINCT.

MALUS IS NOT IGNORANT IN MATTERS OF THE HUMAN SPIRIT. HE KNOWS WE POSSESS A BASIC SENSE OF SELF-PRESERVATION. SURVIVAL PROGRAMS OUR CODE FOR RIGHT AND WRONG.

MALUS CAN'T ERASE THE CODE, SO HE INFECTS IT.

RIGHT AND WRONG ARE NOT THE RULES WHEN YOU'RE A MISTAKE.

SURVIVAL IS POINTLESS WHEN YOU HAVE NO HOPE.

THE TOXIC VIRUS MALUS WEAVES INTO OUR LIVES CANNOT BE REASONED AWAY. DARK MATTER CANNOT BE ERADICATED WITH COUNSELING.

IN ALL MY LIVES, THE ONLY THING I'VE SEEN SAVE PEOPLE FROM THEMSELVES IS HOPE. HOPE BEYOND LOGIC. HOPE BEYOND WHAT THE EYE CAN SEE.

FILLED WITH HOPE, THE HUMAN SPIRIT IS AN INSATIABLE FORCE OF ENERGY, TRANSCENDING BIOLOGY TO EMBRACE SOMETHING ETERNAL.

WITHOUT HOPE, THE SPIRIT DIES AND NOTHING AWAITS BUT DEATH.

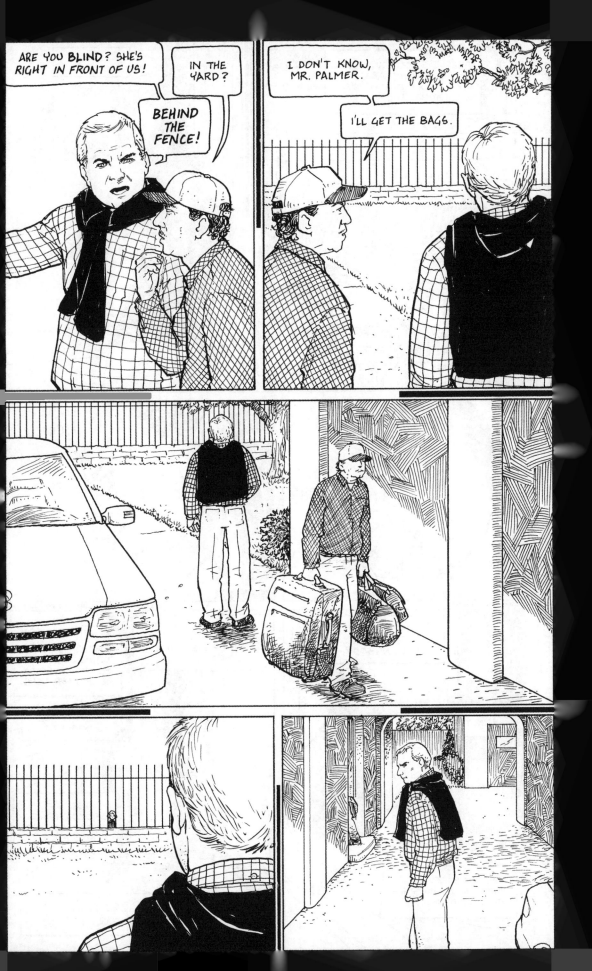

I CAN'T BEGIN TO IMAGINE WHAT LIFE HAS BEEN LIKE FOR LILITH— NEVER DYING, WATCHING ENTIRE CIVILIZATIONS COME AND GO, OVER AND OVER AND OVER AGAIN.

EXCEPT FOR ME, EVERY PERSON SHE'S EVER KNOWN IS DEAD. EVERY PERSON SHE'S EVER CARED ABOUT — DEAD.

FOR LILITH, LIFE AND LOVE ARE ABOUT LOSS. AND THE EARTH IS A GRAVEYARD.

THE MEMORIES ALONE WOULD BE MORE THAN ANYONE COULD BEAR.

BELIEVE ME, IT DOES SOMETHING TO YOU.

IT DOES SOMETHING TO YOU.

SO, SOMETHING TELLS ME LILITH HAD NO PROBLEM "WAKING" ME ALL THOSE TIMES BEFORE BUT, I KEPT SAYING NO TO HER OFFER.

THIS TIME, RATHER THAN LET HER REBOOT ME, I SAID YES.

THIS TIME, I INTEND TO FIND OUT WHAT LILITH REALLY WANTS.

TERRY MOORE

ABSTRACT STUDIO
ISSUE No.
38
3.99 US

RACHEL RISING

"DEATH IS A DIALOGUE BETWEEN
THE SPIRIT AND THE DUST."

—EMILY DICKINSON

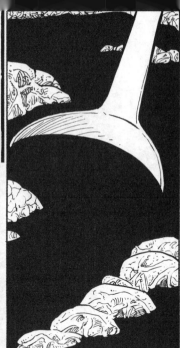

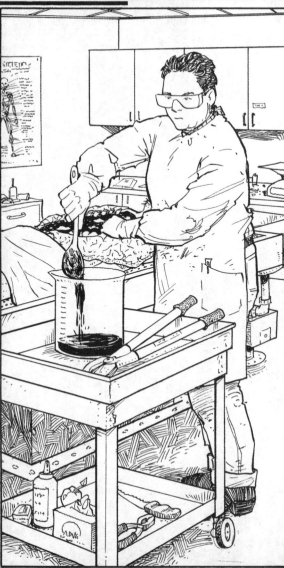

RIGHT. DIDN'T YOU SAY YOU WERE BURIED FACE DOWN?

YES. IT WAS AWFUL, VERY DISORIENTING. WHEN I WOKE UP I COULDN'T TELL WHICH WAY WAS UP.

DO THESE PHOTOS STIR ANY MEMORIES? CAN YOU REMEMBER ANYTHING ABOUT THAT NIGHT OR THE MAN WHO ATTACKED YOU? WHAT DID HE LOOK LIKE? WAS HE BIG? SMALL? WHAT DID HE SOUND LIKE?

I CAN'T...

TRY. WHAT DID YOU SMELL?

WET EARTH... AN OPEN GRAVE.

: SNIFF :

MAYBE YOU DO REMEMBER, RACHEL, BUT IT'S TOO PAINFUL TO RECALL.

I'M SORRY, DEAR, BUT THE MORE INFORMATION YOU CAN GIVE ME, THE SOONER I CAN PUT THAT MAN WHERE HE BELONGS ... ON MY TABLE.

THAT'S A LOVELY THOUGHT.

MMM, LET'S JUST SAY THERE ARE A FEW EXPERIMENTS I'VE ALWAYS WANTED TO TRY IN HERE BUT PROFESSIONAL ETHICS FORBID IT... AND LACK OF AN APPROPRIATE TEST SUBJECT.

SO IF WE CAN GET HIM IN HERE ALIVE... AND CONSCIOUS...

AUNT JOHNNY!

ALL IN THE NAME OF SCIENCE, MY DEAR. PAYBACK IS A BITCH.

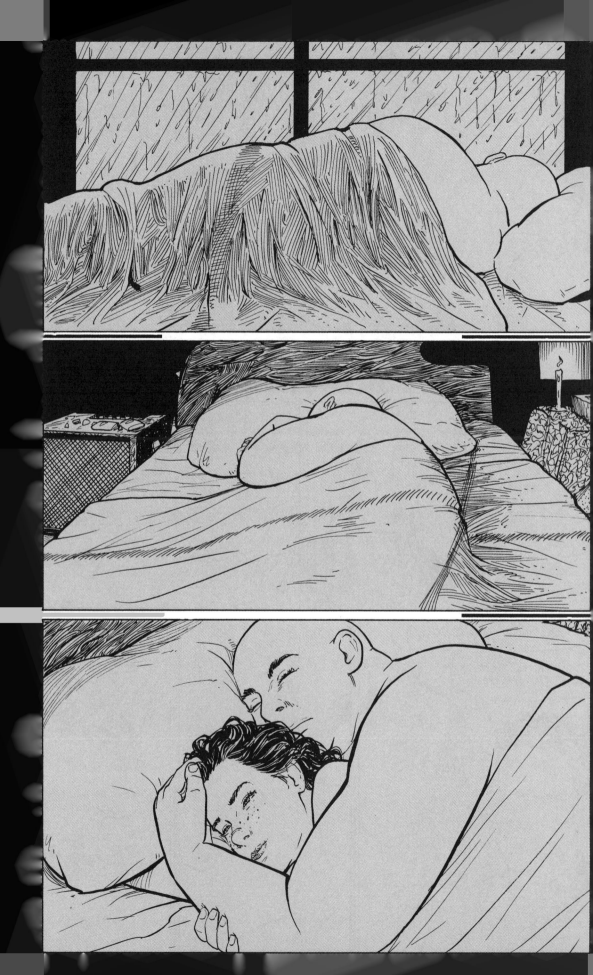

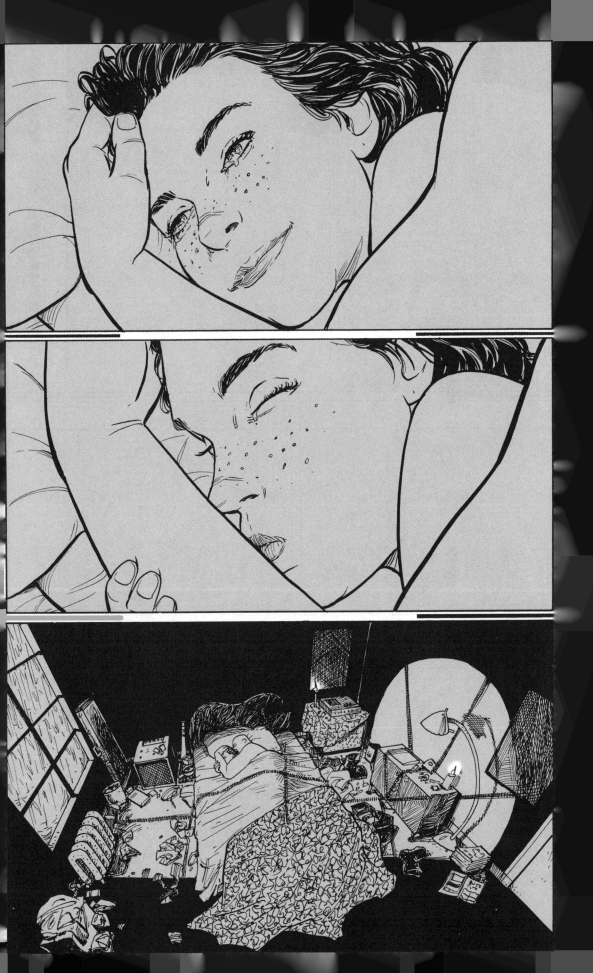

I... I NEED TO SIT DOWN.

LILLIAN, GET HIM A CUP OF WATER.

MY HEART... RACING.

RELAX.

GLUB!

I MUST BE LOSING MY MIND. THAT WAS SIXTY YEARS AGO.

YOU LOOK JUST LIKE HER, EVEN TALK LIKE HER... THE ONLY GIRL I EVER LOVED.

BIGGEST MISTAKE OF MY LIFE — CHOOSING MY INHERITANCE OVER HER.

HERE YOU GO, MR. STRICKLAND.

LILLIAN, TELL YOUR FATHER WE'LL JOIN HIM IN A MINUTE OR TWO.

HERBIE, YOU HAVE A CHANCE TO MAKE IT RIGHT TODAY, BY HELPING THIS COMPANY.

I DON'T UNDERSTAND.

STAY CALM AND I'LL TELL YOU A GREAT SECRET.

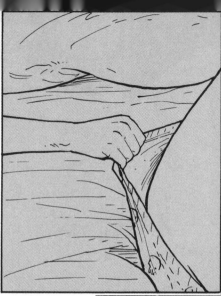

Where you goin'?

I HAVE TO PEE.

YOU'RE GOING WITH ME?

mm hmm.

Earl?

MMM?

Do you think I'm too clingy?

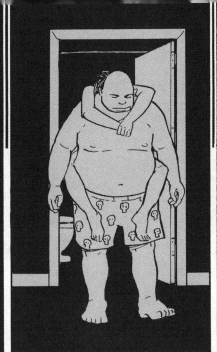

FLUSH!

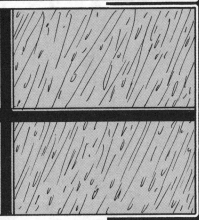

"I SEE YOU."
—MALUS

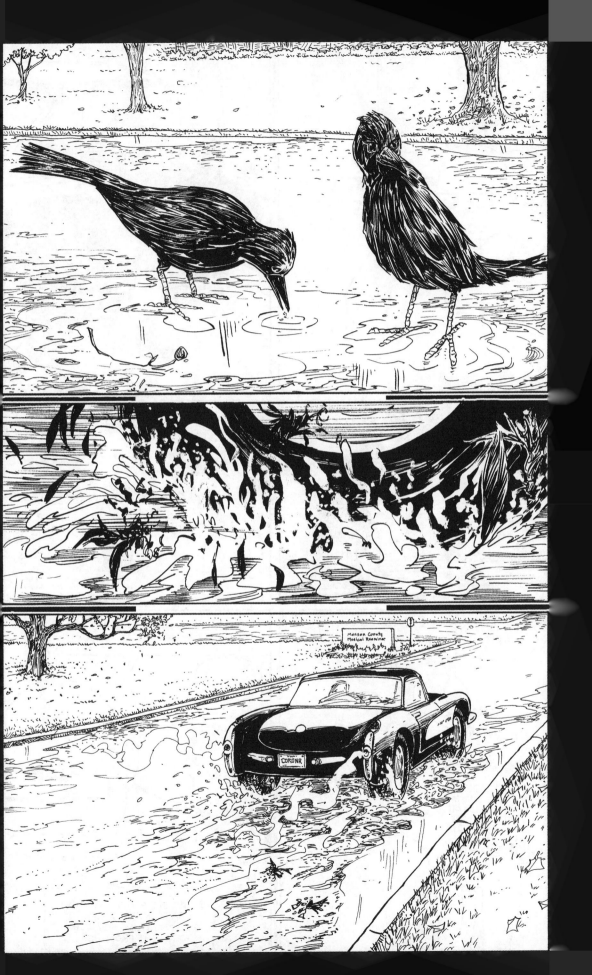

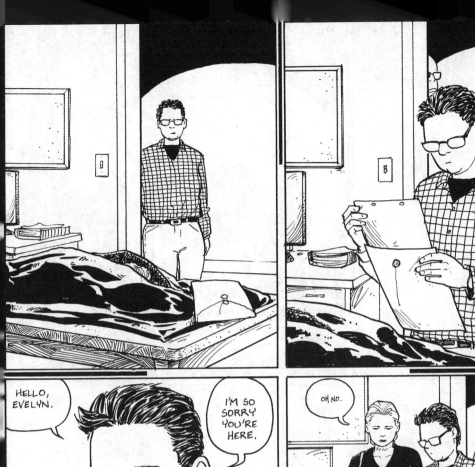

HELLO, EVELYN.

I'M SO SORRY YOU'RE HERE.

OH NO.

WHAT HAPPENED?

HIT AND RUN.

DID THEY CATCH THE DRIVER?

NO.

CHILDREN SHOULD BE OFF LIMITS TO THIS STUFF.

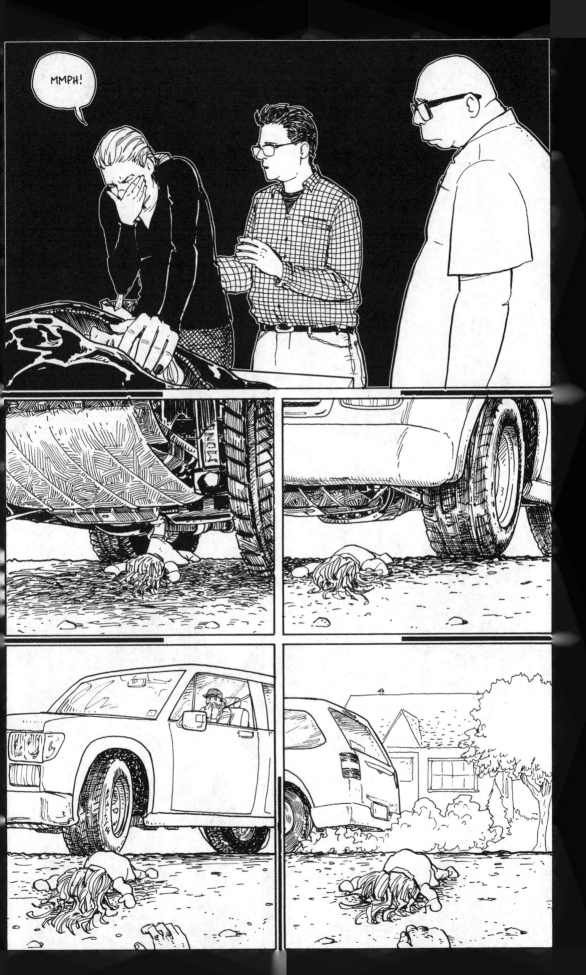

⩗SNIFF!⩖ YOU DON'T DESERVE THIS, SWEETHEART.

RACHEL?

BIG WHITE SUV, MANSON LICENSE PLATE 3B9-2T3. BACKED RIGHT OVER HER.

DID YOU SEE THE DRIVER?

SCHOOL MOM, WHITE, THIRTIES, BALL CAP, PONYTAIL, DYE JOB.

WHAT HAPPENED? WHY...

ON THE PHONE.

OH.

HUH.

PROBLEM?

NOTHING. I'M GETTING NOTHING.

WELCOME BACK TO PLANET EARTH.

I DON'T UNDERSTAND. THERE'S NO LIFE AT ALL.

IT'S LIKE HOLDING A ROCK.

INTERESTING. THIS SHEDS A LITTLE LIGHT ON WHAT YOU TAP INTO, BECAUSE THERE'S A LOT OF SCIENTIFIC DATA HERE.

GUESS I'M NOT VERY SCIENTIFIC.

MAYBE IT'S A MATTER OF TIME. MAYBE THERE IS A DECAY FACTOR TO WHAT YOU TAP INTO ... AND THESE BONES ARE OLDER THAN WE THINK.

OR ... MAYBE YOU NEED MORE ORGANIC TISSUE THAN THIS.

Y'KNOW, SKIN ... MUSCLE ... BODY ORGANS.

OR WHAT'S LEFT OF THEM.

WHAT ARE YOU TALKING ABOUT?

WELL, THERE IS ...

OHHH NO! I'M NOT TOUCHING THE FLOATER! NO WAY! IT'S DISGUSTING!

HE ... HE ... IS THE ONLY OTHER CORPSE WE HAVE RIGHT NOW.

RACHEL, WE NEED TO KNOW. IT'S IMPORTANT!

UGH!

WHAT HAPPENED TO HIS ARMS AND LEGS?

WE DON'T KNOW. MAYBE HIS BONES WILL TELL US.

IF THEY WERE CUT OFF, I'LL PROBABLY FIND MARKS FROM THE BLADE.

AND IF THERE AREN'T ANY MARKS?

THEN, MORE THAN LIKELY, THE FISH ATE OFF HIM UNTIL THE LIMBS DETACHED AND FLOATED AWAY.

THEY TROLLED THE AREA BUT DIDN'T FIND ANYTHING. WE MAY NEVER FIND THEM.

THAT'S SO SAD.

YEAH, I SUPPOSE IT IS.

SO, YOU WANT TO GIVE IT A TRY? MIGHT TELL US A LOT. WHAT DO YOU THINK?

I THINK I LIKED IT BETTER WHEN YOU WERE A SKEPTIC.

"I CAN CALCULATE THE MOTION OF HEAVENLY BODIES,
BUT NOT THE MADNESS OF PEOPLE."

—ISAAC NEWTON

WHAT THE...

OH HELL NO!! JACK, STOP!!

ゲス野郎!

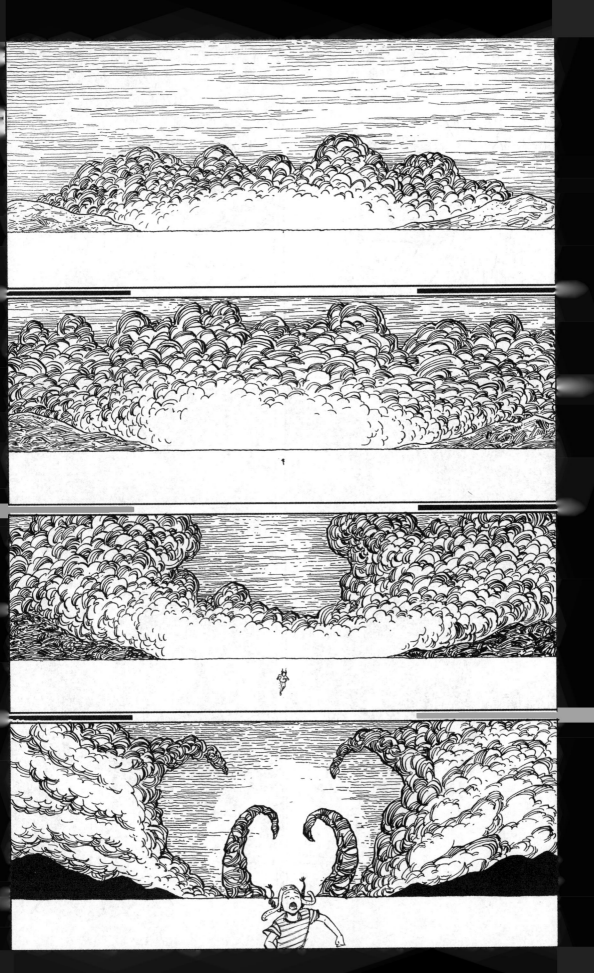

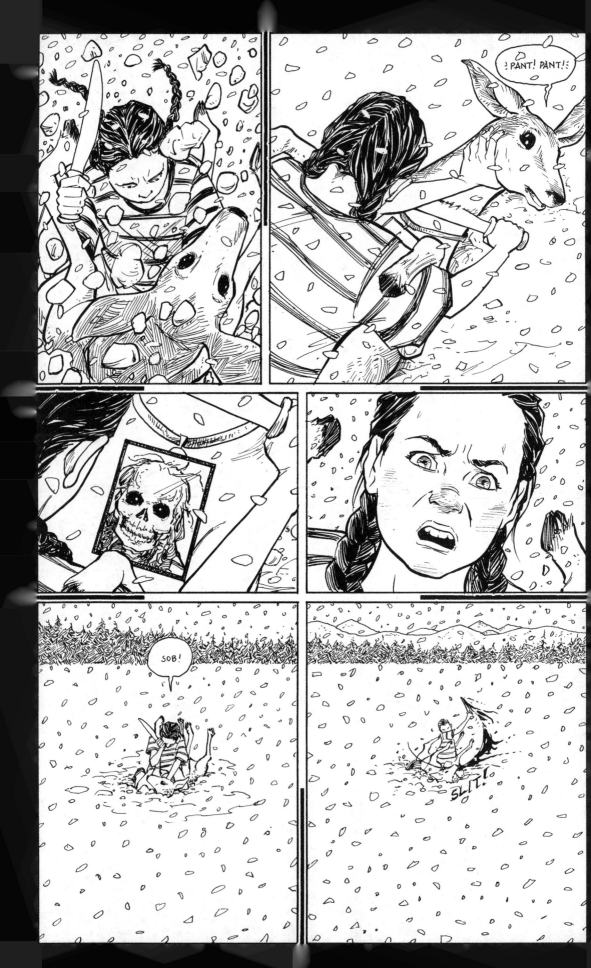

TERRY MOORE

RACHEL RISING

ABSTRACT STUDIO
ISSUE No.
41
3.99 US

"AND THE DEVIL THAT DECEIVED THEM WAS CAST
INTO THE LAKE OF FIRE AND BRIMSTONE, WHERE
THE BEAST AND FALSE PROPHET ARE, AND SHALL BE
TORMENTED DAY AND NGHT FOR EVER AND EVER."

—REVELATION 20:10

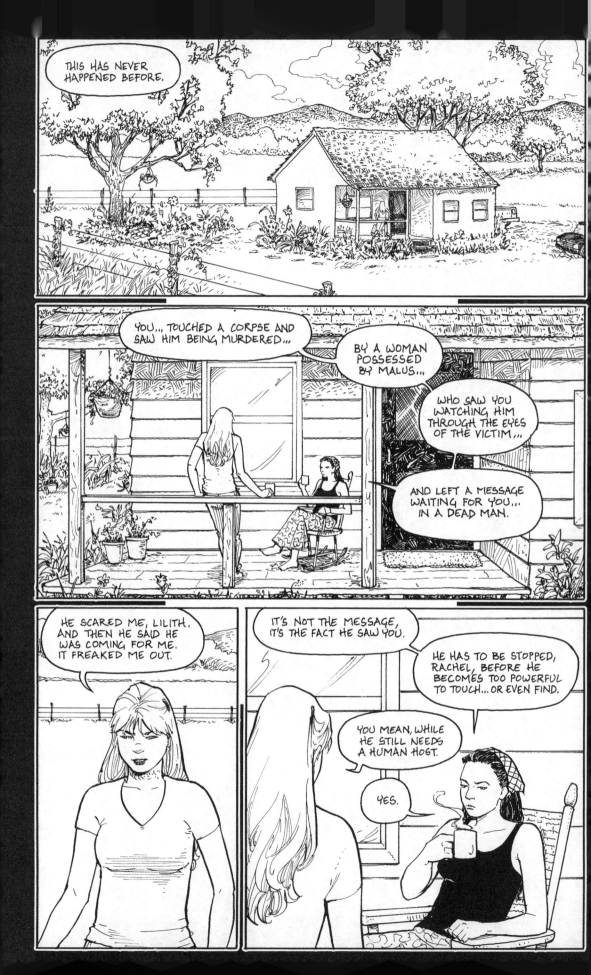

WHERE ARE YOU GOING?

THE RESERVOIR.

IF YOU'RE GOING AFTER MALUS, YOU NEED TO WAIT FOR ME.

NO, I DON'T.

THIS IS MY FAULT—ALL THE GRIEF WE'VE BEEN PUT THROUGH. IT STARTED WITH ME... I'M THE ONE WHO HAS TO END IT.

THEN WHY AM I EVEN HERE? WHY DO YOU KEEP WAKING ME UP TO THIS GODFORSAKEN REALITY?

I'M LONELY.

WHAT?

BECAUSE I'M LONELY, SISTER. IS THAT SO HARD TO UNDERSTAND? YOU'RE THE ONLY ONE I CAN SHARE LIFE WITH, EVERYONE ELSE COMES AND GOES LIKE A PASSING CROWD. WITHOUT YOU, I FEEL LIKE A GHOST.

LILITH!

TAKE CARE OF ZOE.

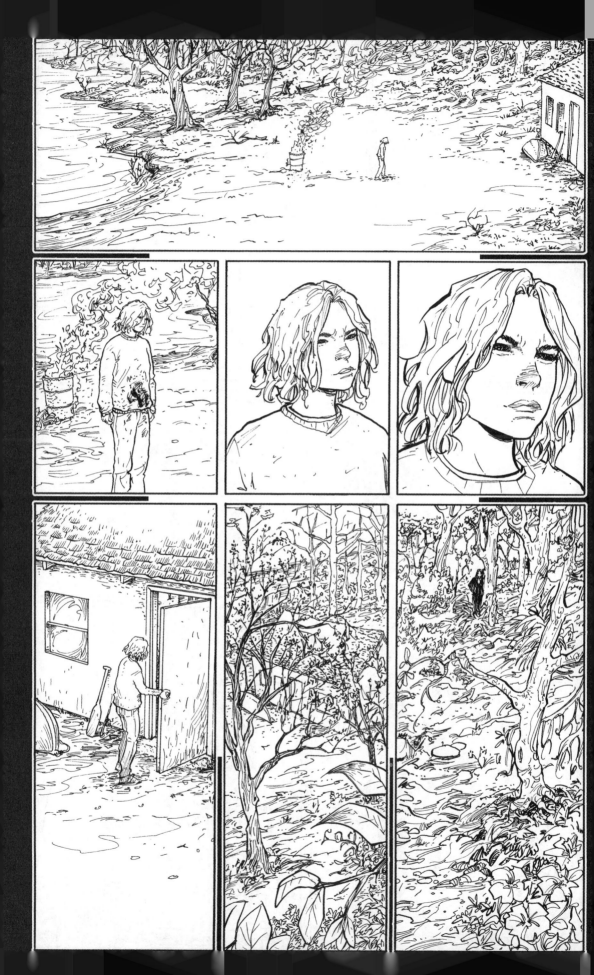

SNAP!

CLAP!

COUGH! COUGH! YOU CAN'T KILL ME WITH WITCHCRAFT, YOU STUPID WHORE!

I KNOW.

I'VE JUST ALWAYS WANTED TO DO THIS.

KRAK!

AAAAGH!

WHY DO YOU PERSECUTE ME, LILITH? I CAN HELP YOU.

I DON'T WANT YOUR HELP. YOU DON'T BELONG HERE, MALUS, TIME TO GO.

YOU CAN'T FIGHT GOD'S PLAN, WOMAN!

YOU LIED TO ME, ANGEL— TRIED TO KEEP ME FROM SEEING THE OBVIOUS—

MY SWORD!?

WHAP!

THIS IS THE PLAN!

SLAM!

KRAK!

BOOM!

"No one knows with regard to death
whether it is not really the greatest
blessing that can happen to man; but
people dread it as though they were
certain it is the greatest evil."

—Plato

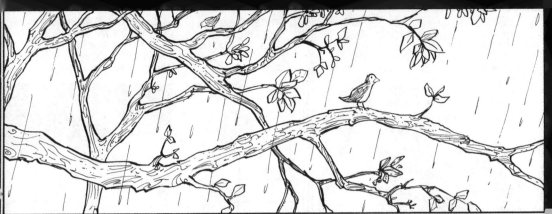

THE BOLT OF LIGHTNING THAT STRUCK MALUS RATTLED WINDOWS ALL OVER MANSON COUNTY. THE WEATHERMAN SAID IT WAS "A TRANSIENT LUMINOUS EVENT." THE FIRST TIME IN RECORDED HISTORY THAT IONOSPHERIC LIGHTNING HAD STRUCK THE GROUND.

IT MAY BE A FIRST FOR HIM, BUT I'VE SEEN IT BEFORE. THE SAME LIGHTNING DROPPED MALUS HERE TO BEGIN WITH.

WIPE ON, WIPE OFF.

LILITH TOLD ME SHE COULDN'T SEE THE BOTTOM OF THE HOLE THE LIGHTNING MADE. "IT WENT ALL THE WAY TO HELL," SHE SAID. BY MORNING, IT WAS GONE, LEAVING AN UGLY SCAR IN A MUDDY FIELD WHERE THE RESERVOIR HAD BEEN.

Mayor's heart attack blamed on thunder ye

GOD IS NOT MOCKED.

SO, THE QUESTION NOW IS,,,

ARE WE FORGIVEN?

DID LILITH SATISFY THE NON-NEGOTIABLE BALANCE THAT NATURE REQUIRES?

DID SHE BREAK THE CURSE THAT HAS KEPT US BOTH ALIVE, EXILED ON EARTH SINCE THE DAWN OF MAN? ARE WE FREE?

CAN WE DIE AT LAST, ONCE AND FOR ALL,,,

AND FINALLY GO HOME?

I MEAN, I KNOW IT'S ALL ABOUT THE PHYSICS, THE POSITIVE AND NEGATIVE OF THINGS, BUT THAT'S WHAT IS SO UNIQUE ABOUT THE HUMAN RACE — WE'RE ABLE TO CHANGE OUR POLARITY. MALUS WAS AN ANGEL AND THEY CAN'T DO THAT. ONLY HUMAN BEINGS CAN.

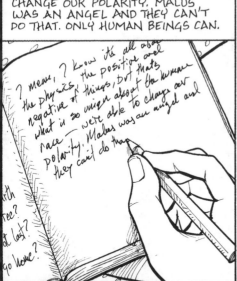

TIME WILL TELL IF WE'RE OFF THE HOOK. I GUESS I'LL FIND OUT THE NEXT TIME I DIE. WILL THE ANGEL OF DEATH TALK TO ME AT LAST? WILL MA MALAI TAKE MY HAND AND WALK ME THROUGH THE MIST?

LILITH, SHE'S A DIFFERENT STORY... A DIFFERENT PUNISHMENT.

I CAN'T IMAGINE WHAT IS AHEAD FOR HER.

BUT WHEN MY SISTER CAME BACK FROM THE RESERVOIR AND TOLD ME WHAT HAPPENED, I WAS SO HAPPY I HUGGED HER AND TOLD HER THAT I LOVED HER. AND LILITH HUGGED ME BACK...FOR THE FIRST TIME SINCE *THE FALL*.

LAST NIGHT, WE SLEPT BENEATH THE STARS AND DREAMED ABOUT THE FUTURE — BECAUSE NOW WE MAY HAVE ONE.

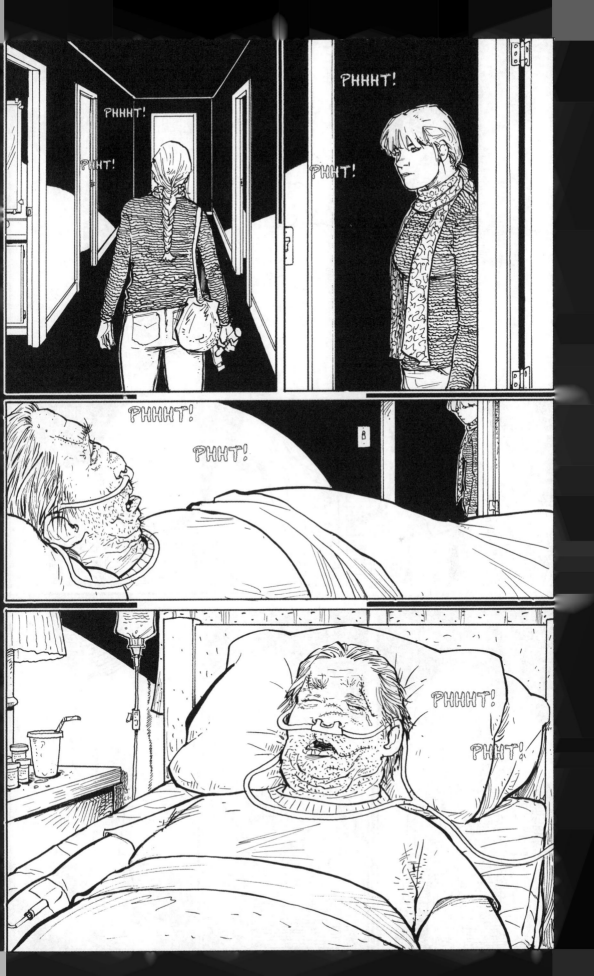

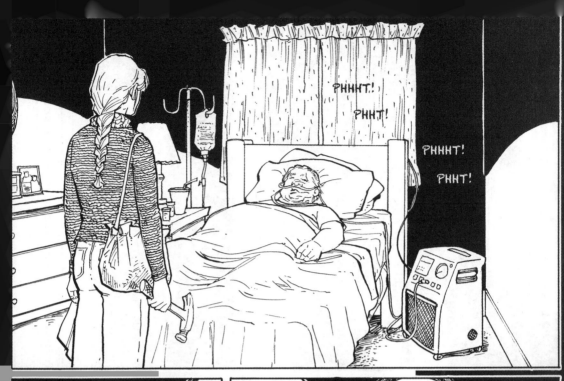

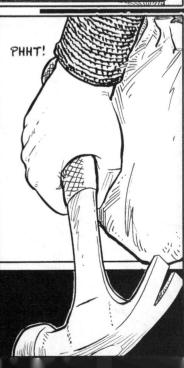

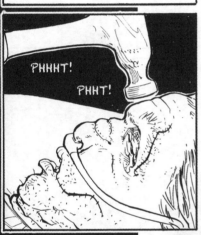

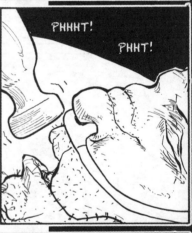

EVERYTHING ALL RIGHT?

YEAH. I'M JUST WALKING HOME FROM THE BLUE NOTE.

ARE YOU RACHEL BECK?

YES.

YOU LIVE ALONE ON WHITE OWL STREET... THE LITTLE GREEN HOUSE... BEDROOM IN THE BACK.

HOW DO YOU KNOW THAT?

BRRRT!

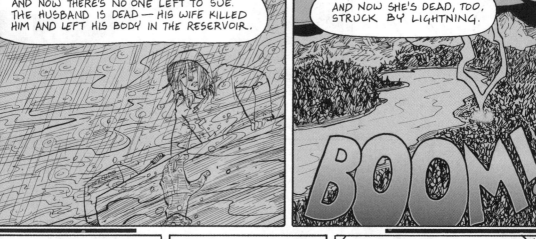

THAT'S A SHEBA MOTH, VIRGIL. THE LAST ONE. THEY'VE BEEN EXTINCT FOR THOUSANDS OF YEARS.

GUESS WHERE SHE LIKES TO LAY HER EGGS.

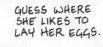

AAARGH!!

THAT INSECT IS GOING TO BURROW DEEP INTO YOUR BRAIN AND LAY HER EGGS ...THOUSANDS OF THEM. WHEN THEY HATCH, THE LARVAE WILL EAT YOU FROM THE INSIDE OUT. UNTIL YOU'RE COMPLETELY HOLLOW.

I'M NOT GOING TO LIE TO YOU, VIRGIL...

IT'S A HORRIBLE WAY TO DIE ... IT TAKES WEEKS.

PHHHT!

PHHT!

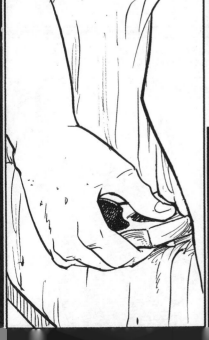

AAAAGH!!

BANG! BANG! BANG!

THE INSTANT HE SHOT ME I KNEW IT WAS FATAL.

MY HEART RACED WILDLY, FILLING MY LUNGS WITH BLOOD. STARS EXPLODED IN MY HEAD AND I WONDERED IF THE SCREAMS I HEARD WERE MINE.

ALL I COULD THINK WAS, NOT HERE. DON'T DIE HERE, IN THIS ROOM, NEXT TO HIM.

GET UP!

GET UP!

WALK.

TO THE LIGHT,

WALK!

GET OUT OF THIS HOUSE.

THAT'S ALL YOU HAVE LEFT TO DO.

GET OUT OF THE HOUSE.

AWAY FROM THESE WRETCHED PEOPLE AWAY FROM THE EVIL.

WHEN I OPENED THE DOOR, THERE SHE WAS, OUTSIDE, WAITING FOR ME.

MA MALAI.

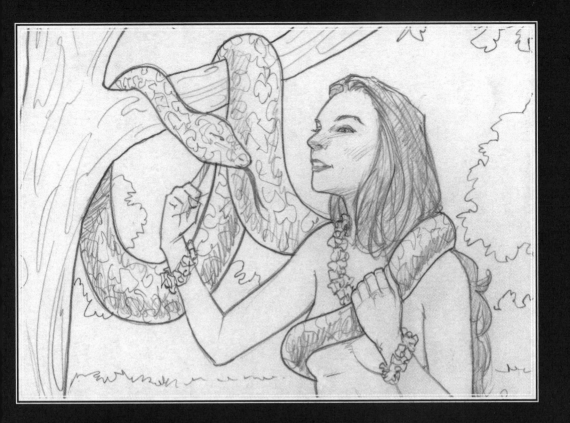

STORY & ART
TERRY MOORE

PUBLISHER
ROBYN MOORE

ABSTRACTSTUDIOCOMICS.COM

TERRYMOOREART.COM
TERRYMOOREART

RACHEL RISING TM©2016 TERRY MOORE. ALL RIGHTS RESERVED.
PUBLISHED BY ABSTRACT STUDIO, INC., P. O. BOX 271487, HOUSTON, TX 77277-1487.
NO PORTION OF THIS PUBLICATION MAY BE REPRODUCED OR TRANSMITTED IN ANY FORM OR BY ANY MEANS
WITHOUT THE EXPRESS WRITTEN PERMISSION OF THE PUBLISHER. NAMES, CHARACTERS, PLACES AND INCI-
DENTS FEATURED IN THIS PUBLICATION ARE EITHER THE PRODUCT OF THE AUTHOR'S IMAGINATION OR ARE
USED FICTITIOUSLY. ANY RESEMBLANCE TO ACTUAL PERSONS (LIVING OR DEAD), EVENTS, INSTITUTIONS OR
LOCALES, WITHOUT SATIRICAL INTENT, IS COINCIDENTAL. BECAUSE IT'S BASICALLY ALL SATIRICAL.
PRINTED IN CANADA

THE RACHEL RISING BOOK SERIES

Shadow Of Death
Fear No Malus
Cemetery Songs
Winter Graves
Night Cometh
Secrets Kept
Dust To Dust

OTHER BOOKS BY TERRY MOORE

Strangers In Paradise
Echo
SIP Kids
Terry Moore's How To Draw